CHRISTMAS 1989.

Happy 1st Christmas Clark,

lots of love from,

auntie Mandy

xxx

# A CHILD'S BOOK OF CHRISTMAS

# A CHILD'S BOOK OF CHRISTMAS

St Michael

This edition published in 1989 exclusively for
Marks and Spencer p.l.c.
Michael House, Baker Street, London W1A 1DN

by Century Benham Ltd
62–65 Chandos Place, London
WC2N 4NW

Designed by Polly Dawes

ISBN 0 7126 3444 4

Printed and bound in Italy
by New Interlitho SpA

# CONTENTS

# Coming up to Christmas

Christmas comes but once a year,
And when it does
It brings good cheer.
Roast beef, plum pudding and mince pie;
Who likes them better than I?

# MERRY CHRISTMAS

Christmas comes! He comes, he comes,
Ushered with a rain of plums;
Hollies in the window greet him;
Schools come driving post to meet him,
Gifts precede him, bells proclaim him,
Every mouth delights to name him;
Curtains, those snug room-enfolders,
Hang upon his million shoulders,
And he has a million eyes
Of fire, and eats a million pies,
And is very merry and wise;
Very wise and very merry,
And loves a kiss beneath the berry.

From the poem by Leigh Hunt

L.M.

# CHRISTMAS IS COMING

Long before the birth of Jesus, holly was considered special. Its glossy green leaves were the sign of spring in the dark days of winter. Even the Romans used holly to decorate their houses during their winter festival, Saturnalia.

There is a legend that the shepherds who went to see Jesus in the stable first put their flocks for safety in a pen made of holly. One small lamb was so determined to see the new baby that he struggled through the thorns. Drops of his blood scattered on the leaves and became bright red holly berries.

Stir Up' Sunday is the day we are supposed to make our Christmas puddings. It is so called because of the prayer for the day, which begins 'Stir up, we beseech Thee, O Lord,' and is nothing to do with stirring up puddings! It always falls in the second half of November. Once, Christmas pudding was made with meat and oatmeal and prunes and this is why it is still called plum pudding. Mince pies, too, were once made with mince meat and the custom of offering them to all visitors, especially travellers, at Christmas, is a very old one.

Why are robins so popular at Christmas? Probably because they are there at a time when other birds have left for warmer countries. There is a legend that when Jesus was born, a robin kept a fire alight in the stable, to keep the baby warm. The little bird worked so hard that he burned his feathers and when Mary saw what had happened, she asked that he should always have a red breast in memory of his kind deed.

Mistletoe was always thought to bring peace and good luck: but no one knows exactly why the custom grew up that any woman standing under the mistletoe branch could be kissed. For every kiss she received, she had to pick one berry – and when there were no more, the kissing had to stop, or it was thought to be very unlucky indeed.

Who was the Lord of Misrule? Several hundred years ago, each of the great households would choose a 'Lord' from amongst the serving men and it was his job to organize the revelries for the Christmas season. Tradition had it that he and his 'court' would be masked and should go unpunished for any act during their 'reign'. This was very unpopular with the authorities because they complained that it led to 'wyld drunkenesse and disorderlye deedes'. Perhaps it did. In any case, it was banned during Puritan times and was never revived.

# CHRISTMAS IS COMING

Christmas is coming
And the goose is getting fat,
Please to put a penny in the old man's hat.
If you haven't got a penny,
A halfpenny will do;
If you haven't got a halfpenny,
God bless you!

Anon.

# CHRISTMAS

The holly in the windy hedge
And round the Manor House the yew
Will soon be stripped to deck the ledge,
The altar, font and arch and pew,
So that the villagers can say
'The church looks nice,' on Christmas Day.

And London shops on Christmas Eve
Are strung with silver bells and flowers
As hurrying clerks the City leave
To pigeon-haunted classic towers,
And marbled clouds go scudding by
The many-steepled London sky.

And girls in slacks remember Dad,
And oafish louts remember Mum,
And sleepless children's hearts are glad,
And Christmas-morning bells say 'Come!'
Even to shining ones who dwell
Safe in the Dorchester Hotel.

And is it true? And is it true,
This most tremendous tale of all,
Seen in a stained-glass window's hue,
A Baby in an ox's stall?
The Maker of the stars and sea
Become a Child on earth for me?

From the poem by John Betjeman

# THE HOLLY AND THE IVY

The holly and the ivy,
When they are both full grown,
Of all the trees that are in the wood,
The holly bears the crown:

The rising of the sun
And the running of the deer,
The playing of the merry organ,
Sweet singing in the choir.

The holly bears a blossom
As white as lily flower,
And Mary bore sweet Jesus Christ
To be our sweet Saviour:

The holly bears a prickle
As sharp as any thorn,
And Mary bore sweet Jesus Christ
On Christmas Day in the morn:

The holly bears a bark
As bitter as any gall,
And Mary bore sweet Jesus Christ
For to redeem us all.

The holly and the ivy,
When they are both full grown,
Of all the trees that are in the wood,
The holly bears the crown.

From the traditional carol

J.C.S.

# SNOW-BOUND

Shut in from all the world without,
We sat the clean-winged hearth about,
Content to let the north wind roar
In baffled rage at pane and door,
While the red logs before us beat
The frost-line back with tropic heat;
And ever, when a louder blast
Shook beam and rafter as it passed,
The merrier up its roaring draught
The great throat of the chimney laughed.

From the poem by John Greenleaf Whittier

L. L.

# THE NUTCRACKER

THE STORY OF TCHAIKOVSKY'S
FAMOUS CHRISTMAS BALLET

It was Christmas Eve in a small town in Germany and snow lay thick on the ground. A family was in the middle of a Christmas party. The room glowed with rich colours, red, gold, green and silver and a long table was covered with Christmas food. There were puddings, jellies, cakes and crisp, sugary mince pies.

Six or seven children were fluttering eagerly around the Christmas tree, hunting for their presents. 'Toy soldiers! Look!' shouted Fritz. 'Just what I wanted.'

'Dancing shoes for me!' cried Clara, his sister.

Suddenly, there was a gust of cold air. A tall stranger stood in the doorway, wearing a long, black cloak. 'Doctor Drosselmeyer!' said someone, as they recognized Clara's godfather. 'Come in!' The doctor smiled: he moved his hands swiftly, like a magician. Two footmen brought in a pair of dolls, a boy and a girl, dressed like clowns. The doctor wound the dolls up and they sprang immediately into a wild dance.

'More! More!' cried the children, spellbound. The doctor put his hand under his cloak and drew out a large, wooden nutcracker. It was painted to look like a soldier and dressed in red, with a stiff scarlet feather in its helmet. A dozen eager hands shot up to grasp the beautiful toy: but the doctor reached over their heads to give the nutcracker to Clara.

'Another present for me?' said Clara, delighted.

Fritz was jealous. 'Let me see it,' he cried and snatched it out of her hands.

'It's mine!' shouted Clara in tears as Fritz ran off. Suddenly he tripped and the nutcracker flew out of his hands. It fell onto the floor and smashed in pieces. Clara wept bitterly and refused to be comforted. But soon, it was time for bed and the children were sent upstairs. The doctor wished everyone a goodnight and gently laid the broken nutcracker under the Christmas tree before sweeping out as mysteriously as he had arrived.

The whole house slept. Then Clara awoke with a start. Her nutcracker; was it really broken? She crept downstairs. The house was full of moving shadows and the parlour door creaked as she opened it. The curtains fluttered as if some trapped animal struggled behind them. Suddenly, there was a whirring, clicking sound and the owl in the grandfather clock flapped its wings and began striking twelve o'clock.

Clara shivered. A shadow fell over the brightly-lit Christmas tree. In a second it vanished. Clara blinked; for the nutcracker seemed to mend itself before her eyes and come to life. He smiled at her; but before she could say a word, an army of great, grey mice poured into the parlour, led by the terrible seven-headed Mouse King.

The nutcracker sprang to his feet and shouted 'to arms!' To Clara's amazement, Fritz's toy soldiers leaped out of their box, waving their swords. Row after row passed her, marching towards the mice and soon there was a terrifying battle. Rifles cracked, and the floor was filled with seething, shrieking fighters.

Clara watched anxiously as her nutcracker at last met the Mouse King in single combat. The nutcracker fought bravely; but he was no match for the cunning Mouse King. The King pretended to slip, and the nutcracker lowered his sword.

'Look out!' cried Clara, as the Mouse King leapt to his feet, his teeth bared. Without thinking, Clara seized one of her dancing shoes and threw it as hard as she could at the mouse. It hit him and he fell stunned. The nutcracker grabbed his sword and again the soldiers charged. Soon the mice turned and fled and the Mouse King lay dead on the floor. Clara cheered and the nutcracker bent down to pick up her dancing shoe. He turned and Clara gasped. He was a real, live prince.

'You saved my life,' he said. 'The Mouse King was a wicked magician who turned me into a nutcracker. By his death I am released from the spell.' The prince smiled. 'But now you must visit my kingdom.'

The prince waved his arm and the walls fell away. He and Clara were in the middle of a beautiful, snowy landscape. Flakes fell softly, sparkling as they touched their clothes. Suddenly, Clara saw that the shining shapes were fairies, glittering as they clustered round them in the moonlight.

'You're lovely!' cried Clara, laughing as they fluttered round her more and more, until she could hardly see through the whirling flakes. The air was filled with the sweetest music, as if some fairy orchestra was playing on instruments of ice.

'Is this your kingdom?' asked Clara.

The prince shook his head as an elegant carriage made of carved walnut shell rolled up. He offered Clara his hand and they climbed in.

Clara had hardly had time to be sad at leaving the silver snow fairies when the carriage rolled through an enormous archway – made of huge blocks of Turkish Delight. The gates were dark chocolate studded with giant raisins and almonds. 'It's all made of sweets!' cried Clara.

'Of course,' said the prince. 'We are now in my kingdom, the Land of Spun Sugar.'

Just then, the Sugar Plum Fairy appeared in a glistening robe of pink silk frosted with sugar. On her head was a crown of stars, which sparkled as she moved. She waved her wand and immediately, Clara could see dozens of cooks singing as they whipped and stirred and decorated. 'We are making a feast in your honour, Princess Clara,' said the Fairy in a voice as clear as a peal of bells. 'Because you have saved the life of our dear prince.'

A table appeared like magic, set with dishes of crystal sugar and the cooks began to bring on the food; ice creams like towers and castles, cascades of jellies, fruit, sweets and creams as light as froth and a giant tree made of sugar filled with lollies of every colour and flavour.

As they ate, a crowd of jostling sweets arrived, giggling like school children and to Clara's astonishment, they began at once to dance.

First, the milk and dark chocolates did a fiery Spanish dance. Then three little marzipan shepherdesses stepped forward and played a cheerful tune on the pipes. A coffee cream was a brilliant acrobat, leaping and dancing and turning somersaults in the air. Finally, a huge, multicoloured confection, called Mother Ginger leaped on to the stage. She lifted her enormous, hooped skirts and a score of tiny sweets wriggling and laughing like little children came bounding out. Finally, the Sugar Plum Fairy herself gave a dance so delicate and airy it seemed that she might float away. Clara was entranced. She had never in her life seen anything so beautiful.

'Come, my dear,' said the Prince, gently. 'It is nearly daybreak and it would never do for your family to find you missing.' Suddenly, Clara felt terribly tired. She nodded and yawned and as if by magic, the walnut carriage rolled into the hall. The Prince led Clara lightly to her seat and kissed her goodbye. 'Goodbye! Goodbye!' waved all the sweets and as Clara sank back into the seat, she fell into a deep sleep.

When she awoke, she was in her bed at home. 'Was I dreaming?' she wondered sleepily. 'Or was that the best Christmas surprise I have ever had?'

But no matter how hard she looked, there was no sign of the Prince, or her beautiful toy, the nutcracker.

M.D.Spooner

# THE CHERRY TREE CAROL

Joseph was an old man
And an old man was he,
When he wedded Mary
In the land of Galilee.

Joseph and Mary
Walked through an orchard green,
Where were berries and cherries
As thick as might be seen.

O then spoke up Mary,
With words so meek and mild,
'Pick me one cherry, Joseph,
For I am with child.'

O then spoke up Joseph,
In rage and fury,
'Let the father of the baby
Gather cherries for thee!'

O then spoke the baby
Within his mother's womb –
'Bow down then the tallest tree
For my mother to have some.'

Then bowed down the highest tree,
Unto his mother's hand.
Then she cried, 'See, Joseph,
I have cherries by command.'

O eat your cherries, Mary,
O eat your cherries now,
O eat your cherries, Mary,
That grow upon the bough.

From the traditional carol

# CHRISTMAS IS COMING

ABRIDGED FROM *A COUNTRY CHILD* BY
ALISON UTTLEY

At Christmas the wind ceased to moan. Snow lay thick on the fields and the woods cast blue shadows across it. The fir trees were like sparkling, gem-laden Christmas trees, the only ones Susan had ever seen. The orchard, with the lacy old boughs outlined with snow, was a grove of fairy trees. The woods were enchanted, exquisite, the trees were holy, and anything harmful had shrunken to a thin wisp and had retreated into the depths.

Footprints were everywhere on the snow, rabbits and foxes, blackbirds, pheasants and partridges, trails of small paws, the mark of a brush, and the long feet of the cock pheasant and the tipmark of his tail.

A jay flew out of the wood like a blue flashing diamond and came to the grass-

plot for bread. A robin entered the house and hopped under the table while Susan sat very still and her father sprinkled crumbs on the floor.

On the kitchen walls hung the sides of bacon and from hooks in the ceiling dangled great hams and shoulders. Bunches of onions were twisted in the pantry and barn, and an empty cowhouse was stored with potatoes for immediate use.

The floor of the apple chamber was covered with apples, rosy apples, little yellow ones, like cowslip balls, wizenedy apples with withered, wrinkled cheeks, fat, well-fed smooth-faced apples, and immense green cookers, pointed like a house, which would burst in the oven and pour out a thick cream of the very essence of apples.

Even the cheese chamber had its cheeses this year, for there had been too much milk for the milkman, and the cheese presses had been put into use again. Some of them were Christmas cheese, with layers of sage running through the middles like green ribbons.

In the little dark wine chamber under the stairs were bottles of elderberry wine, purple, thick, and sweet, and golden cowslip wine, and hot ginger,

some of them many years old, waiting for the winter festivities.

There were dishes piled with mince pies on the shelves of the larder, a row of plum puddings with their white calico caps, and strings of sausages, and round pats of butter, with swans and cows and wheat-ears printed upon them.

Everyone who called at the farm had enough to eat and drink that Christmas.

L. L.

# WASSAIL SONG

Here we come a-wassailing
Among the leaves so green,
Here we come a-wandering,
So fair to be seen.

Love and joy come to you,
And to you your wassail true,
And God bless you, and send you
A happy New Year,
And God send you
A happy New Year.

Our wassail cup is made
Of the rosemary tree,
And so is your beer
Of the best barley.

We are not daily beggars
That beg from door to door,
But we are neighbours' children
Whom you have seen before.

We have got a little purse
Of stretching leather skin;
We want a little of your money
To line it well within.

Bring us out a table,
And spread it with a cloth;
Bring us out a mouldy cheese,
And some of your Christmas loaf.

God bless the master of this house,
Likewise the mistress too;
And all the little children
That round the table go.

Traditional song from the north of England

# WASSAILING

Wassailing comes straight out of Old England when wassail meant, roughly speaking, 'your health'.

Throughout Christmas it was the custom to keep a wooden wassail bowl simmering on the hearth. It was a sort of rich punch; and one recipe – with the comforting name of 'lamb's wool' – included hot ale, spices and sugar, as well as roasted apples, which floated on top.

Young people would go in bands from door to door with a bowl, singing and offering a drink to their neighbours. It was supposed to be good luck to have a taste; and even luckier to reward the singers with food or to fill up their bowl.

Carol singers today are given a hot drink and a mince pie!

# BOBBING FOR APPLES

This simple game is great fun and can be played by grown ups and children alike. It is much harder than it looks and until you get the knack, you will get nothing for your efforts except water up the nose; so do keep a supply of towels handy.

Half-fill a large bowl with water and float in it about twenty small apples, remembering that the more apples there are, the easier it is. Each person in turn has his or her hands tied behind their back with a handkerchief. Then the player kneels at the bowl and tries to take out the apples with his teeth. If your bowl is big enough, two or more can play at once which is more exciting (but be careful not to crack heads or drown).

The winner is, of course, the person who takes out the most apples.

# THE NIGHT BEFORE CHRISTMAS

'Twas the night before Christmas,
When all through the house
Not a creature was stirring,
Not even a mouse.

# CHRISTMAS EVE

There are many traditions about Christmas Eve: some older than Christmas itself, some quite modern. Some we have forgotten and some are just as popular as ever.

At the stroke of midnight on Christmas Eve, all animals are supposed to be able to talk to each other. Some claim that if you were born as the clock was striking, you can understand every word they say. In any case, midnight was the time when goblins, ghouls and witches no longer had power to hurt humans. Everyone used to stay up late on Christmas Eve, frightening each other with scarey stories, safe in the knowledge that on this night, at least, they could come to no harm.

It is considered terribly unlucky to turn away strangers on Christmas Eve. What if one of them was the Christ Child in disguise?

If a girl wanted to know more about her future husband, she had to knock on the door of a pigsty on Christmas Eve. If a grown pig grunted, she would marry an older man. If a piglet squealed, she would have a young husband! Another test that was said to be foolproof was for a girl to make a dumb cake on Christmas Eve. In complete silence, she would make a cake out of salt, barley and wheatmeal, prick her initials on it and put it in the oven. She would then open the door and wait for the stroke of midnight. If she was lucky, her future husband would walk in and they would eat the cake together. It can't have been very delicious – but perhaps they didn't care.

Branches of fir have been used – with other evergreens – as Christmas decorations for hundreds of years. However, it was not until Victorian times that people in England began to bring whole trees indoors and hang them with coloured balls, candles and stars.

There is a story that long ago, a widow had no money at Christmas time to spend on her children, but she was determined that they should, at least, have a tree. She brought indoors a small fir tree and decorated it with a few coloured scraps before going to bed with a heavy heart. The Christ Child saw how sad she was and beckoned to a couple of spiders. They scuttled over to the tree and began to weave the most beautiful shining threads from twig to twig. The children awoke to see their dark tree glistening and sparkling like silver. And the widow's name? It was Tinsel!

Few people have a fireplace big enough for a proper Yule Log today; but we do still eat chocolate 'yule logs'. Burning the Yule Log is another ancient custom, much older than Christmas, and it belongs to the old Winter Festival which was held on the shortest day of the year. People burned a huge log to encourage the sun to come back. Traditionally, it was lit on Christmas Eve from a piece from the previous year and had to be kept burning throughout the twelve days of celebrations.

# SANTA CLAUS

He comes in the night! He comes in the night!
He softly, silently comes;
While the little brown heads on the pillows so white
Are dreaming of bugles and drums.
He cuts through the snow like a ship through the foam,
While the white flakes around him whirl;
Who tells him I know not, but he findeth the home
Of each good little boy and girl.

The little red stockings he silently fills,
Till the stockings will hold no more;
The bright little sleds for the great snow hills
Are quickly set down on the floor.
Then Santa Claus mounts to the roof like a bird,
And glides to his seat in the sleigh;
Not the sound of a bugle or drum is heard
As he noiselessly gallops away.

Anon.

# THE FATHER CHRISTMAS ON THE CAKE

For fifty weeks I've languished
Upon the cupboard shelf,
Forgotten and uncared for,
I've muttered to myself.
But now the year is closing,
And Christmastime is here,
They dust me down and tell me
To show a little cheer.
Between the plaster snowman
And little glassy lake
They stand me in the middle
Of some ice-covered cake,
And for a while there's laughter,
But as the week wears on,
They cut up all the landscape
Till every scrap is gone.
Then with the plaster snowman
And little lake of glass
I'm banished to the cupboard
For one more year to pass.

Colin West

# THE STONES

ABRIDGED FROM *THE LEGEND OF THE STONES OF PLOUHINEC* BY BARBARA LEONIE PICARD

In parts of Brittany are found groups of great stones known as menhirs, arranged in circles or in avenues, like tall, rough-hewn pillars. Country people will tell you that long ago they were set up by the kerions, the fairy dwarfs, and that beneath many of them the kerions hid their treasure.

Near the little town of Plouhinec, close by the Breton coast, there lies a barren stretch of moor where only coarse grass grows, and the yellow broom of Brittany. On this plain stand the stones of Plouhinec, two long rows of them.

On the edge of the moor there once lived a farmer with his sister Rozennik. Rozennik was young and pretty and she had many suitors from Plouhinec, yet she saved her smiles for Bernez, a poor lad who worked on her brother's farm. But the farmer refused to consider Bernez as a suitor until he could show him his pockets full of gold.

One Christmas Eve, while the farmer was feasting his men in the farmhouse kitchen, as was his yearly custom, there came a knock on the door. Outside in the cold wind stood an old beggar who asked for a meal and shelter for the night. He looked a sly, artful old rogue and one whom it would have been unwise to trust, but, because it was Christmas Eve, he was made welcome and given a bowl of soup and a place by the fire. After supper the farmer took him out to the stable and said he might sleep there, on a pile of straw. In the stable were the ox who drew the farmer's plough and the donkey who carried to market whatever the farmer had to sell.

The beggar was just falling asleep when midnight struck and, as everyone knows, at midnight on Christmas Eve, all the beasts in the stable can speak to each other, in memory of the first Christmas in the stable at Bethlehem.

'It is a cold night,' said the donkey.

As soon as the old beggar heard the donkey speak, he pretended to be asleep and snoring, but he kept very wide awake, for it was a habit with him, wherever he could, to listen to other people talking, in case he heard something to his advantage, which he might put to profitable purpose.

'No colder,' replied the ox, 'than it

will be on New Year's Eve when the stones of Plouhinec go down to the river to drink and leave their treasure uncovered. Only once in every hundred years that comes to pass.' The ox looked down at the beggar, snoring on the straw. 'If this old man knew what we know, he would be off, seven nights from now, to fill his pockets from the kerions' hoard.'

'Small good it would do him,' said the donkey, 'unless he carried with him a bunch of crowsfoot and a five-leaved trefoil. Without those plants in his hand, the stones would crush him when they returned.'

'Even the crowsfoot and the five-leaved trefoil would not be enough,' said the ox, 'for, remember, whosoever takes the treasure of the stones must offer in exchange a Christian soul, or the stolen treasure will turn to dust. And though a man may easily find crowsfoot, and he may, if he searches long enough, find a five-leaved trefoil, where will he find a Christian man willing to die for him?'

'That is true enough,' agreed the donkey; and the two beasts went on to talk of other matters.

The old beggar had heard enough to make him determined to steal the treasure and he was up and away from the farm at the first light of day. For six days he searched all about the countryside for crowsfoot and trefoil. He found the crowsfoot soon enough and he found trefoil, but none with more than three leaves; until on the very last day but one of the old year, he found a five-leaved trefoil. Eagerly he hurried back to Plouhinec, reaching the town on the next morning, and went at once to the moor, that he might spy out a spot for himself as near to the stones as possible to be close at hand when they went, at midnight, down to the river.

But he found someone there before him. Young Bernez had brought his midday meal of bread and cheese to eat sitting alone beneath the largest of the stones whilst he dreamt of Rozennik.

Having finished his meal, he was spending the few spare minutes that remained to him before he had to return to work in idly carving a cross upon the stone by which he sat.

'What are you doing?' asked the old beggar, who recognized him as one of the men from the farmhouse where he had spent Christmas Eve.

Bernez smiled. 'This holy sign may be of help or comfort to someone one day. It is as good a way as any of passing an idle moment, to carve a cross on a stone.'

'That is so,' replied the beggar; but while he was speaking he was remembering the look in Bernez' eyes as he had watched Rozennik at the feasting on Christmas Eve, for his own sharp eyes missed little. A cunning thought came into his head. 'What would you do,' he asked, 'if you had your pockets full of gold?'

'Why,' said Bernez, 'that is easy. I would go to the farmer and ask for Rozennik for my wife. He would not refuse me then, and I think she would not say no to me.'

The beggar looked about him and leant his head close to Bernez. 'I can tell you how to fill your pockets with gold, and a sack or two besides.'

'How?' asked Bernez, surprised. And the beggar told him what he had learned from the ox and the ass; all save how a bunch of crowsfoot and a five-leaved trefoil were necessary if one was not to be crushed by the stones as they returned from the river, and how a Christian soul must be offered in exchange for the gold. When he had finished, Bernez' eyes shone and he clasped the old man's hand. 'You are a good friend indeed, to tell me this and to share your good fortune with me. I will meet you here before midnight.' He finished his carving joyfully and ran back to his work on the farm; whilst the beggar chuckled to himself at the thought of how easily he had found someone to die in exchange for the gold.

Before midnight they were waiting together, Bernez and the old beggar, hidden behind a clump of broom in the darkness. No sooner had midnight struck than there was a noise as of a great thundering, the ground shook and the huge stones heaved themselves out of the earth and began to move down to the river. 'Now,' said the beggar, 'this is the moment.'

They ran forward and looked down into the pits where the stones had stood and, there at the bottom of each pit, was a heap of treasure. The beggar opened the sacks he had brought with him and began to fill them hastily, one after the other; but Bernez, his heart full

M.D. SPOONER

of the thought of Rozennik, filled only his pockets with gold.

It seemed no more than a moment later that the earth began to tremble and the ground echoed as though to the tramp of a giant army marching. The stones, having drunk from the river, were returning to their places. Bernez cried out in horror as he saw them loom out of the darkness, 'Quickly, quickly, or we shall be crushed to death.'

The old beggar laughed and held up his bunch of crowsfoot and his five-leaved trefoil. 'Not I', he said, 'for I have these magic plants to protect me. But you, you are lost, and it is as well for me, since unless a Christian soul is given in exchange, my treasure will crumble away in the morning.'

With terror Bernez heard him and saw that he had spoken the truth, for the first of the stones moved aside when it reached the beggar and his magic herbs, and after it the other stones passed on either side of him, leaving him untouched, to move close together as they came near to Bernez.

The young man was too afraid to try to escape. He covered his face with his hands and waited when he saw the largest stone of all bear down on him. But above the very spot where Bernez crouched, trembling, the stone paused and remained there, towering over him, as though to protect him, while all the other stones had to move aside and so pass him by. And when Bernez, amazed, dared to look up, he saw that the stone which sheltered him was the stone upon which he had carved a cross.

Not until all the other stones were in their places did it move, and then it went by Bernez and on to where its own pit showed dark, with shining treasure at the bottom. On its way it overtook the beggar, stumbling along with his heavy sacks of gold. He heard it come after him and held out the bunch of crowsfoot and the five-leaved trefoil with a triumphant shout. But because of the cross carved upon it, the magic herbs no longer had any power over the stone and it went blindly on its way, crushing the old beggar beneath it. And so it passed on to its own place and settled into the earth again until another hundred years should have gone by.

Bernez ran back home to the farm, as fast as his legs could carry him; and, when in the morning he showed his pockets full of gold, the farmer did not refuse to give him his sister. And as for Rozennik, she did not say no, for she would have had him anyway, had the choice rested with her.

# HARK! THE HERALD ANGELS SING

Hark! the herald angels sing
Glory to the new-born King;
Peace on earth and mercy mild,
God and sinners reconciled:
Joyful all ye nations rise,
Join the triumph of the skies,
With the angelic hosts proclaim,
Christ is born in Bethlehem:

Hark! the herald angels sing
Glory to the new-born King.

From the traditional carol

# OLLIE IN WINTER

ABRIDGED FROM *OLLIE'S SKI TRIP*
BY ELSA BESKOW

On Ollie's sixth birthday, his father gave him a pair of new skis. He hadn't had proper skis before, so you can guess how much he wanted to try them out. But winter didn't seem to want to come that year. Ollie watched and waited and wondered, 'Will it ever come?'

At last, a week or two before Christmas, snow began falling in big flakes, and it went on for two whole days and nights without stopping. Everything was covered with a thick, white blanket. And when Ollie woke on the third morning, the sky was shining blue and the snow sparkled like millions of stars.

Ollie was so excited, he went head over heels three times on his bed without stopping. He scrambled into his clothes, not caring if they went on the right way round or not. Then he ran in to see his mother.

'Mum, Mum, can I go out *now*, this minute?'

'Listen,' said his mother. 'You must have some breakfast first. And don't forget your mittens.' She stuffed a sandwich into both pockets, and told him that he could stay out until dinner time. Then he waved goodbye and, fastening on his new skis, he skied over the thick, white snow towards the forest.

The trees were so pretty! It was like going into an enchanted palace; and Ollie said to himself, 'Thank you, King Winter. I'm so glad you came!'

The next moment he almost fell over backwards with surprise, for there in front of him stood an old man, glittering white from head to toe. Ollie stared at him. 'Are you King Winter?' he asked.

'Oh no,' said the old man, 'I'm only Jack Frost. What do you think of the forest today?'

'Did you do it?' asked Ollie. 'How did you make it all sparkle?'

'It's easy,' said Jack Frost, and he breathed on Ollie's coat. His breath hung like a white cloud; and when it disappeared, Ollie's coat was covered with glistening hoar frost.

Then he laughed. 'You're a sharp lad,' he said, 'and I don't think you mind if the cold wind stings your face a bit. You called out King Winter's name a moment ago, so maybe you'd like to come with me to his palace here in the forest?'

'Oh, yes, please!' said Ollie. So off they went through the forest, Jack Frost first and Ollie following.

Before long, they came to a huge castle. It was built of snow and guarded by two polar bears. The bears sniffed at Jack Frost like friendly dogs as he and Ollie walked through the gate way. Then they went across a courtyard and through an iron-studded door made of polished ice.

They came into a huge room. At the

far end, two walruses stood beside a throne of ice. There sat King Winter; and his calm face looked stern. For the first time, Ollie felt a little afraid.

But Jack Frost led him up to the throne. 'This is a very nice boy, Your Majesty,' he said. 'A little while ago, he was so pleased that you had arrived that he was calling your name in the forest.'

Then King Winter smiled, and his eyes gleamed like the Northern lights.

'I'm glad to hear it,' he said. 'You do know how to ski, I suppose?'

'Oh, yes,' said Ollie.

'And toboggan?'

'Yes. Head first and feet first and sideways, too!' said Ollie.

'And skate?'

'I haven't got any skates,' said Ollie.

'No reason why you shouldn't have some,' said King Winter. 'But now that you're here, would you like to look round my palace?'

He nodded to Ollie and Ollie bowed a very deep bow and followed Jack Frost into the next room.

This looked like a big workshop, and some children were building skis and toboggans and sledges; while in one corner, others were making skate blades. They all worked so fast and Ollie watched and wished that he was as clever with his hands as they were.

'Why are you so busy?' Ollie asked one of the boys.

'Well, we've got to hurry now to get finished by Christmas,' said the boy. 'You see, everyone wants their presents for Christmas. But we'll be going out to play in a moment.'

Just then, a gong sounded and all the children streamed out, sweeping Ollie along with them.

And what a time he had! Everyone wanted to play with Ollie and he joined in with everything. First, they skied down a slope with big dips in it; then they taught Ollie to skate on the pond. Next they built snowmen and a big snowcastle that they all stormed and soon there was a huge snow fight, with snowballs flying about in all directions.

All of a sudden, there was a loud whistle and in a flash the children had disappeared back inside the palace, leaving Ollie standing by himself, panting and hot.

'Had a good time?' asked Jack Frost, appearing suddenly.

'Oh, yes!' said Ollie.

'That's good,' said Jack Frost, with a pleased smile.

Then he harnessed a reindeer, stepped on to Ollie's skis, and with Ollie holding on behind him, they drove off.

At the edge of the trees, Jack Frost said good bye. Ollie arrived home so full of what had happened that he could scarcely eat a thing.

And, would you believe it? On Christmas morning, Ollie heard a knock at his window. He tried to look out, but he couldn't see a thing because the glass was covered with the loveliest frost flowers. But he knew at once that Jack Frost had paid him a visit. He went out on to the porch, and there lay a neatly-wrapped parcel. In it was a pair of magnificent skates.

# MR POOTER SENDS A CHRISTMAS CARD

ABRIDGED FROM *DIARY OF A NOBODY* BY
GEORGE AND WEEDON GROSSMITH

Mr Pooter's diary appeared in the magazine *Punch* at the end of the last century and his owlish innocence makes for the best in English humour. In this extract, he joins in the then current craze for sending Christmas cards. As you can see, the Post Office, then as now, were warning people to 'post early for Christmas'.

DECEMBER 20: Went to Smirksons', the drapers, in the Strand, who this year have turned out everything in the shop and devoted the whole place to the sale of Christmas cards. Shop crowded with people, who proceeded to take up the cards rather roughly, and, after a hurried glance at them, throw them down again. I remarked to one of the young persons serving, that carelessness appeared to be a disease with some purchasers. The observation was scarcely out of my mouth, when my thick coat-sleeve caught against a large pile of expensive cards in boxes one on top of the other, and threw them down.

The manager came forward, looking very much annoyed, and picking up several cards from the ground, said to one of the assistants, with a palpable side-glance at me: 'Put these amongst the sixpenny goods; they can't be sold for a shilling now.' The result was, I felt it my duty to buy some of these damaged cards.

I had to buy more and pay more than intended. Unfortunately, I did not examine them all, and when I got home I discovered a vulgar card with a picture of a fat nurse with two babies and the words: 'We wish Pa a Merry Christmas.' I tore up the card and threw it away. *Carrie said the great disadvantage of going out in Society and increasing the number of our friends was, that we should have to send out nearly two dozen cards this year.

DECEMBER 21: To save the postman a miserable Christmas, we follow the example of all unselfish people, and send out our cards early. Most of the cards had fingermarks, which I did not notice at night. I shall buy all future cards in the daytime.
**Lupin (who, ever since he has had the appointment with a stock and share broker, does not seem over-scrupulous in his dealings) told me never to rub out the pencilled price on the backs of the cards. I asked him why. Lupin said: 'Suppose your card is marked 9d. Well, all you have to do is to pencil a 3 – and a long down-stroke after it – in front of the ninepence, and people will think you have given five times the price for it.'

DECEMBER 24: I am a poor man, but I would gladly give ten shillings to find out who sent me the insulting Christmas card I received this morning. I never insult people; why should they insult me? The worst part is, that I find myself suspecting all my friends. The handwriting on the envelope is evidently disguised, sloping the wrong way.

Lupin denied all knowledge of it, and I believe him; although I disapprove of his laughing and sympathizing with the offender. Mr Franching would be above such an act; and I don't think any of the Mutlars would descend to such a course. I wonder if Pitt, that impudent clerk at the office, did it? Or Mrs Birrell, the charwoman, or Burwin-Fosselton? The writing is too good for the former.

* Carrie is Mr Pooter's long-suffering and devoted wife.
** Lupin is Mr Pooter's son. His real name is Willie but he thinks that 'Lupin' is much smarter. In case you are wondering, the upsetting Christmas card was not, in fact, meant for Mr Pooter at all, but for Lupin, being sent by one of his son's 'friends' as a joke. . . .

# CHRISTMAS ON THE RIVERBANK

ABRIDGED FROM *THE WIND IN THE WILLOWS*
BY KENNETH GRAHAME

Rat and Mole have arrived at Mole's house on Christmas Eve; but everything looks empty, dusty and dismal. Mole is depressed and embarrassed but Rat is determined to cheer him up.

* * *

'What a capital little house this is!' Mr Rat called out cheerily. 'Everything here and everything in its place! We'll make a jolly night of it. The first thing we want is a good fire; I'll see to that – I always know where to find things. Now, I'll fetch the wood and the coals, and you get a duster, Mole, and try and smarten things up a bit. Bustle about, old chap!'

Encouraged by his inspiring companion, the Mole roused himself and dusted and polished with energy and heartiness, while the Rat running to and fro with armfuls of fuel, soon had a cheerful blaze roaring up the chimney. He hailed the Mole to come and warm himself; but Mole promptly had another fit of the blues, dropping down on a couch in dark despair and burying his face in his duster.

'Rat,' he moaned, 'how about your supper, you poor, cold, hungry, weary animal? I've nothing to give you – nothing – not a crumb.'

'What a fellow you are for giving in!' said the Rat reproachfully. 'Why, only just now I saw a sardine-opener on the kitchen dresser, quite distinctly; and everybody knows that means there are sardines about somewhere in the neighbourhood.'

They went hunting through every cupboard and turning out every drawer. The result was not so very depressing after all, although of course it might have been better; a tin of sardines – a box of captain's biscuits, nearly full – and a German sausage encased in silver paper.

'There's a banquet for you!' observed the Rat, as he arranged the table. 'I know some animals who would give their ears to be sitting down to supper with us tonight!'

'No bread!' groaned the Mole dolorously; 'no butter, no –'

'No pâté, no champagne!' continued the Rat, grinning. 'And that reminds me – what's that little door at the end of the passage? Your cellar, of course! Every luxury in this house! Just you wait a minute.'

He made for the cellar door, and presently re-appeared, somewhat dusty, with a bottle of beer in each paw and

another under each arm. 'This is really the jolliest little place I ever was in,' he said. 'Now, wherever did you pick up those prints? Make the place look so home-like, they do. No wonder you're so fond of it, Mole. Tell us all about it, and how you came to make it what it is.'

Then, while the Rat busied himself fetching plates, and knives and forks, and mustard which he mixed in an egg-cup, the Mole related – somewhat shyly at first, but with more freedom as he warmed to his subject – how this was got through a windfall from an aunt, and that was a wonderful find and a bargain, and this other thing was bought out of laborious savings and a certain amount of 'going without'. Rat, who was desperately hungry but strove to conceal it, nodded seriously, and said, 'Wonderful', and 'Most remarkable', at intervals.

At last the Rat succeeded in decoying him to the table, and had just got seriously to work with the sardine-opener when sounds were heard from the forecourt without – sounds like the scuffling of small feet in the gravel and a confused murmur of tiny voices, while broken sentences reached them – 'Now, hold the lantern up a bit, Tommy – clear your throats first – no coughing after I say one, two, three. – Where's young Bill? – Here, come on, do, we're all a-waiting –'

'What's up?' inquired the Rat, pausing in his labours.

'I think it must be the field-mice,' replied the Mole, with a touch of pride in his manner. 'They go round carol-singing regularly at this time of the year. They're quite an institution in these parts. And they never pass me over – they come to Mole End last of all; and I used to give them hot drinks, and supper sometimes, when I could afford it. It will be like old times to hear them again.'

'Let's have a look at them!' cried the Rat, jumping up.

It was a pretty sight that met their eyes when they flung the door open. Lit by the dim rays of a horn lantern, some eight or ten little field-mice stood in a semi-circle, red worsted comforters round their throats, their forepaws thrust deep into their pockets, their feet jigging for warmth. With bright, beady eyes they glanced shyly at each other, sniggering a little, sniffing and applying coat-sleeves a good deal. As the door opened, one of the elder ones that carried the lantern was just saying, 'Now then, one, two, three!' and forthwith their shrill little voices uprose on the air, singing one of the old-time carols:

*Villagers all, this frosty tide,*
*Let your doors swing open wide,*
*Though wind may follow, and snow beside,*
*Yet draw us in by your fire to bide;*
*Joy shall be yours in the morning!*

*Here we stand in the cold and the sleet,*
*Blowing fingers and stamping feet,*
*Come from far away you to greet,*
*You by the fire and we in the street,*
*Bidding you joy in the morning!*

*Goodman Joseph toiled through the snow –*
*Saw the star o'er a stable low;*
*Mary she might not further go –*
*Welcome thatch, and litter below!*
*Joy was hers in the morning!*

*And when they heard the angels tell*
*Who were the first to cry Nowell?*
*Animals all, as it befell,*
*In the stable where they did dwell!*
*Joy shall be theirs in the morning.*

The voices ceased, the singers, bashful but smiling, exchanged sidelong glances.

'Very well sung, boys!' cried the Rat heartily. 'And now come along in, all of you, and warm yourselves by the fire, and have something hot!'

'Yes, come along, field-mice,' cried the Mole eagerly. 'This is quite like old times! Shut the door after you. Pull up that settle to the fire. Now, you just wait a minute, while we – O, Ratty!' he cried in despair, plumping down on a seat, with tears impending. 'Whatever are we doing? We've nothing to give them!'

'You leave all that to me,' said the masterful Rat. 'Here, you with the lantern! Come over this way. I want to talk to you. Now, tell me, are there any shops open at this hour of the night?'

'Why, certainly,' replied the field-mouse respectfully. 'At this time of the year our shops keep open to all sorts of hours.'

'Then look here!' said the Rat. 'You go off at once, you and your lantern, and you get me –'

Here much muttered conversation ensued, and the Mole only heard bits of it, such as – 'Fresh, mind! – no, a pound of that will do – see you get Buggins's, for I won't have any other – no, only the best – if you can't get it there, try somewhere else – yes, of course, home-made, no tinned stuff – well then, do the best you can!' Finally, there was a chink of coin passing from paw to paw, the field-mouse was provided with an ample basket for his purchases, and off he hurried, he and his lantern.

The rest of the field-mice, perched in a row on the settle, their small legs swinging, gave themselves up to the enjoyment of the fire, and toasted their chilblains till they tingled; while the Mole plunged into family history and made each of them recite the names of his numerous brothers, who were too young, it appeared, to be allowed to go out a-carolling this year, but looked forward very shortly to winning the parental consent.

The Rat, meanwhile, was busy examining the label on one of the beer-bottles. 'I perceive this to be Old Burton,' he remarked approvingly. 'Sensible Mole! The very thing! Now we shall be able to mull some ale! Get the things ready, Mole, while I draw the corks.'

It did not take long to prepare the brew and thrust the tin heater well into the red heart of the fire; and soon every field-mouse was sipping and coughing and choking (for a little mulled ale goes a long way) and wiping his eyes and laughing and forgetting he had ever been cold in all his life.

'They act plays too, these fellows,' the Mole explained to the Rat. 'Make them up all by themselves, and act them afterwards. And very well they do it, too! They gave us a capital one last year, about a field-mouse who was captured at sea by Barbary corsair, and made to row in a galley; and when he escaped and got home again, his lady-love had gone into a convent. Here, you! You were in it, I remember. Get up and recite a bit.'

The field-mouse addressed got up on his legs, giggled shyly, looked round the room, and remained absolutely tongue-tied. His comrades cheered him on, Mole coaxed and encouraged him, and the Rat went so far as to take him by the shoulders and shake him; but nothing could overcome his stage-fright. Then the latch clicked, the door opened, and the field-mouse with the lantern reappeared, staggering under the weight of his basket.

There was no more talk of play-acting once the very real and solid contents of the basket had been tumbled out on the table. Under the generalship of Rat, everybody was set to do something or to fetch something.

In a very few minutes supper was ready, and Mole, as he took the head of the table in a sort of dream, saw a lately barren board set thick with savoury comforts; saw his little friends' faces brighten and beam as they fell to without delay; and then let himself loose – for he was famished indeed – thinking what a happy home-coming this had turned out, after all. As they ate, they talked of old times, and the field-mice gave him the local gossip up to date, and answered as well as they could the hundred questions he had to ask them.

They clattered off at last, very grateful and showering wishes of the season, with their jacket pockets stuffed with remembrances for the small brothers and sisters at home. When the door had closed on the last of them and the chink of the lanterns had died away, Mole and Rat kicked the fire up, drew their chairs in, brewed themselves a last nightcap of mulled ale, and discussed the events of the long day. At last the Rat, with a tremendous yawn, said, 'Mole, old chap, I'm ready to drop. Sleepy is simply not the word. That your own bunk over on that side? Very well, then, I'll take this. What a ripping little house this is! Everything so handy.'

He clambered into his bunk and rolled himself well up in the blankets, and fell immediately asleep.

The weary Mole also was glad to turn in without delay, and soon had his head on his pillow, in great joy and contentment.

A Rackham

# IN THE BLEAK MID-WINTER

In the bleak mid-winter
Frosty winds made moan,
Earth stood hard as iron
Water like a stone.
Snow had fallen, snow on snow,
Snow on snow
In the bleak mid-winter
Long ago.

Enough for Him, whom cherubim
Worship night and day,
A breastful of milk and a manger full of hay;
Enough for Him whom angels
Fall down before,
The ox and ass and camel
Which adore.

What can I give Him
Poor as I am?
If I were a shepherd
I would bring a lamb;
If I were a Wise Man
I would do my part;
Yet what I can, I give Him,
Give my heart.

From the carol by Christina Rossetti

MDSpooner

# CHRISTMAS AMONG THE SAVAGES

ABRIDGED FROM *CHRISTMAS WITH THE SAVAGES*
BY LADY MARY CLIVE

We looked through into the ballroom, which was blazing with light from dozens of candles. In the middle stood an immense Christmas tree, glittering, sparkling, dazzling.

'O-o-ooh!' we all said.

I can see us joining hands and dancing round the tree, and I can see Mr O'Sullivan walking about with a sponge on the end of a long stick with which he put out any dangerous candles, and I can see a work-basket lined with red satin which I suppose was my present, and I can see the fairy doll at the top which I wanted but didn't get – no one got it.

And then somehow we were upstairs again in the twilight of our bedrooms eating our suppers and chattering. We all had a glass of milk, and a ginger biscuit and a marie biscuit, which could either be eaten one at a time or together like a sandwich. Both ways made a lot of crumbs.

Peggy ran into my room to swap her marie for my ginger and I ran into hers to borrow a big safety-pin (you can probably guess what for). Marguerite had remembered to pack one of my father's stockings but not a safety-pin.

Then I heard the Savages giggling so much that I had to run into their room to see what was happening. Harry had fallen out of bed and Nana Savage had said, 'Get back to bed, you silly little fellow,' but he continued to lie on the floor, laughing and unable to move. The nurses were all rather keen to hurry us along, as later in the evening there was to be dancing.

Then our own candles were blown out and we were left lying in the dark to wait for Father Christmas. We were all excited but in different ways, from Tommy who was so horrified and revolted by the idea of a dreadful old man coming down the chimney in the middle of the night that they had to hang his stocking outside his door, to Lionel who had put a wet sponge beside his bed with the worst intentions. I was in that state when you don't know what to expect or whom to believe, and I several times crept to the end of my bed to feel my limp stocking. Was it possible that in a few hours' time that dingy, woollen object would be oozing toys?

Just as I was dropping off to sleep I

was roused by the sound of the Savages' door being violently thrown open and bare feet pattering along the passage.

'Nana!' wailed Harry, 'Minnie! May! My stocking's empty! There's nothing in it!'

Loud, unfeeling laughter burst from the nursery and presently Harry was led back to bed by Minnie, who explained gently that though he had been asleep, it wasn't morning.

I was glad Harry had made such a disturbance as I had been getting very drowsy myself and I did really mean to lie awake till Father Christmas came so as to settle once and for all who he was. But the room was pitch dark except for a strip of light under the door, and it was very difficult to keep my eyes open. I could not see the pictures of stags but I wondered what they would think of reindeer. 'Is Father Christmas a Cavalier or a Roundhead? And suppose he has hooks instead of hands, and hooks instead of feet, and wears a pink sash. . . .'

Presently I noticed that the crack of light wasn't there any more, and as I lay in the dark I became aware of a strong smell of oranges. Vaguely I wondered where the smell was coming from and then, with a start, I asked myself, could it be coming from my stocking?

Regardless of the cold, I pushed back the bedclothes and crawled to the end of my bed and my hand met something that was woolly, hard and sharp. Nothing else in the world feels quite like a well-stuffed stocking.

With a sigh of relief I nipped back under the bedclothes thinking, 'The Magic has worked yet once again. He has come.'

ROSA C. PETHERICK.

# HANG UP BABY'S STOCKING

Hang up the baby's stocking.
Be sure you don't forget.
The dear little dimpled darling,
She never saw Christmas yet.
But I've told her all about it,
And she opened her big blue eyes,
And I'm sure she understood it –
She looked so funny and wise.

Dear, what a tiny stocking.
It doesn't take much to hold such little pink toes
As baby's, away from the frost and cold.
But then, for the baby's Christmas,
It will never do at all.
Why! Santa wouldn't be looking for anything half so small.

I know what I'll do for the baby.
I've thought of the very best plan.
I'll borrow a stocking of Grandma's;
The longest that ever I can.
And you'll hang it by mine, dear mother,
Right here in the corner, so!
And leave a letter to Santa,
And fasten it to the toe.

Write – this is the baby's stocking
That hangs in the corner here.
You never have seen her, Santa,
For she only came this year.
But she's just the blessed'st baby.
And now before you go,
Just cram her stocking with goodies,
From the top clean down to the toe!

Anon.

# O LITTLE TOWN OF BETHLEHEM

O little town of Bethlehem,
How still we see thee lie.
Above thy deep and dreamless sleep
The silent stars go by.
Yet in thy dark streets shineth
The everlasting light;
The hopes and fears of all the years
Are met in thee tonight.

O morning stars together
Proclaim the holy birth,
And praises sing to God the King,
And peace to men on earth;
For Christ is born of Mary
And gathered all above,
While mortals sleep, the angels keep
Their watch of wondering love.

From the traditional carol

# CHRISTMAS DAY

Away in a manger, no crib for a bed
The little Lord Jesus
Lay down his sweet head.

# LOVE CAME DOWN AT CHRISTMAS

Love came down at Christmas,
Love all lovely, Love Divine;
Love was born at Christmas,
Star and angels gave the sign.

From the poem by Christina Rossetti

# I SAW THREE SHIPS

I saw three ships come sailing in,
On Christmas Day, on Christmas Day,
I saw three ships come sailing in,
On Christmas Day in the morning.

And what was in those ships all three?

Our saviour Christ and his lady.

Pray, whither sailed those ships all three?

O, they sailed into Bethlehem,
On Christmas Day, on Christmas Day,
O, they sailed into Bethlehem,
On Christmas Day in the morning.

From the traditional carol

# For Them

Before you bid, for Christmas' sake,
  Your guests to sit at meat,
Oh please to save a little cake
  For them that have no treat.

Before you go down party-dressed
  In silver gown or gold,
Oh please to send a little vest
  To them that still go cold.

Before you give your girl and boy
  Gay gifts to be undone,
Oh please to spare a little toy
  To them that will have none.

Before you gather round the tree
  To dance the day about,
Oh please to give a little glee
  To them that go without.

Eleanor Farjeon

# A CHRISTMAS RIDDLE

Flour of England, fruit of Spain,
Met together in a shower of rain;
Put in a bag, tied round with a string;
If you tell me this riddle,
I'll give you a ring.

Answer: Plum pudding

Traditional

# CHRISTMAS BELLS

I heard the bells on Christmas day
Their old familiar carols play
And wild and sweet
The words repeat
Of 'Peace on earth, good will to men!'

From the poem by Henry Wadsworth Longfellow

# MY NAUGHTY LITTLE SISTER AT CHRISTMAS

ABRIDGED FROM *THE NAUGHTIEST STORY OF ALL*
BY DOROTHY EDWARDS

This is such a terrible story about my naughty little sister that I hardly know how to tell it to you. It is all about one Christmas time when I was a little girl, and my naughty little sister was a very little girl.

Now, my naughty little sister was very pleased when Christmas began to draw near, because she liked all the excitement of the plum puddings and the turkeys and the crackers and the holly, and all the Christmassy-looking shops; but there was one very awful thing about her – she didn't like to think about Father Christmas at all – she said he was a horrid old man!

One day, my school teacher said that a Father Christmas Man would be coming to school to bring presents for all the children, and my teacher said that the Father Christmas Man would have toys for all our little brothers and sisters as well, if they cared to come along for them. She said that there would be a real Christmas tree with candles on it.

Wasn't that a nice thought? Well, now, when I told my little sister about the Christmas tree, she said, 'Oh, nice!'

But when I told her about the Father Christmas Man, she said, 'Don't want *him*, nasty old man.'

Still, my mother said, 'You can't go to the Christmas tree without seeing him, so if you don't want to see him all that much, you will have to stay at home.'

But my naughty little sister did want to go, very much, so she said, 'I will go, and when the horrid Father Christmas Man comes in, I will close my eyes.'

When we got to the school, my naughty little sister was very pleased to see all the pretty paper-chains hung all round the classrooms, and when she saw all the little lanterns, and the holly and all the robin redbreast drawings pinned on the blackboards she smiled and smiled. She was very smiley at first.

Then, when some of the teachers came round with the bags of sweets, tied up in pretty coloured paper, my little sister smiled even more, and she sang too when all the children sang. She sang 'Away in a Manger', because she knew the words very well. When she didn't know the words of some of the singing, she 'la-la'd'.

After all the singing there was the Christmas tree, all lit up with candles and shining with silvery stuff, and little

shiny, coloured balls. There were lots of toys on the tree, and all the children cheered and clapped. My little sister looked at the tree, and she looked at the toys, and she saw a specially nice doll with a blue dress on, and she said, 'For me.'

My mother said, 'You must wait and see what you are given.'

Then, as we waited and listened, we heard a tinkle-tinkle bell noise, and the schoolroom door opened, and in walked the Father Christmas Man. My naughty little sister had forgotten all about him, so she hadn't time to close her eyes before he walked in. However, when she saw him, my little sister stopped smiling and began to be stubborn.

The Father Christmas Man was very nice. He said he hoped we were all having a good time, and we all said 'yes', except my naughty little sister – she didn't say a thing.

Then he said, 'Now, one at a time, children; and I will give each one of you a toy.'

So, first of all each school child went up for a toy, and my naughty little sister still didn't shut her eyes because she wanted to see who was going to have the specially nice doll in the blue dress. But none of the school children had it.

Then Father Christmas began to call the little brothers and sisters up for presents, and, as he didn't know their names, he just said, 'Come along, sonny,' if it were a boy, and 'Come along, girlie,' if it were a girl. The Father Christmas Man let the little brothers and sisters choose their own toys off the tree.

When my naughty little sister saw this, she was so worried about the specially nice doll, that she thought that she would just go up and get it. She said, 'I don't like that horrid old beardy man, but I do like that nice doll.'

So, my naughty little sister got up without being asked to, and she went right out to the front where the Father Christmas Man was standing, and she said, 'That doll, please,' and pointed to the doll she wanted.

The Father Christmas Man laughed and all the teachers laughed, and the other mothers and the school children, and all the little brothers and sisters. My mother did not laugh because she was so shocked to see my naughty little sister going out without being asked to.

The Father Christmas Man took the specially nice doll off the tree, and he handed it to my naughty little sister and he said, 'Well, now, I hear you don't like me very much, but won't you just shake hands?'

And my naughty little sister said, 'No.' But she took the doll all the same.

The Father Christmas Man put out his nice old hand for her to shake and be friends, and do you know what that naughty, bad girl did? *She bit his hand!* Can you think of anything more dreadful and terrible? She bit Father Christmas' good old hand, and then she turned and ran out of the school with all the children staring after her, and her doll held very tight in her arms.

The Father Christmas Man was very nice, he said it wasn't a hard bite, only a frightened one, and he made all the children sing songs together.

When my naughty little sister was brought back by my mother, she said she was very sorry, and the Father Christmas Man said, 'That's all right, old lady,' and my funny little sister went right up to him and gave him a big 'sorry' kiss, which pleased him very much.

And she hung her stocking up after all, and that kind man remembered to fill it for her.

My little sister kept the specially nice doll until she was quite grown up. She called it Rosy-Primrose and although she was sometimes bad-tempered with it, she really loved it very much indeed.

# AWAY IN A MANGER

Away in a manger, no crib for a bed,
The little Lord Jesus laid down his sweet head.
The stars in the bright sky looked down where he lay
The little Lord Jesus asleep on the hay.

The cattle are lowing, the baby awakes.
But little Lord Jesus no crying he makes.
I love thee, Lord Jesus! Look down from the sky,
And stay by my side until morning is nigh.

Be near me Lord Jesus, I ask thee to stay
Close by me for ever, and love me, I pray.
Bless all the dear children in thy tender care,
And fit us for heaven to live with thee there.

Traditional

# When all the World Is Full Of Snow

I never know
just where to go,
when all the world
is full of snow.

I do not want
to make a track,
not even
to the shed and back.

I only want
to watch and wait,
while snow moths settle
on the gate,

and on the ice
the boulders ride,
like sleeping snow geese
on the tide.

I only want
myself to be
as silent as
a winter tree,

to hear the swirling
stillness grow,
when all the world
is full of snow.

From the poem by N. M. Bodecker

# A CHRISTMAS CAROL

ABRIDGED FROM A *CHRISTMAS CAROL*
BY CHARLES DICKENS

Here are two extracts from the famous story by Charles Dickens about Scrooge, the miser, who has a miraculous change of heart, due to the ghosts of Christmas Past, Christmas Present and Christmas Yet to Come.

* * *

Oh! But he was a tight-fisted hand at the grindstone was Scrooge! A squeezing, wrenching, grasping, scraping, clutching, covetous old sinner! External heat and cold had little influence on him. No warmth could warm, no cold could chill him. No wind that blew was bitterer than he, no falling snow was more intent upon its purpose, no pelting rain less open to entreaty. Foul weather didn't know where to have him. The heaviest rain and snow and hail and sleet could boast of the advantage over him in only one respect – they often 'came down' handsomely, and Scrooge never did. . . .

Once upon a time – of all the good days in the year, upon a Christmas Eve – old Scrooge sat busy in his counting house. It was cold, bleak, biting, foggy weather; and the city clocks had only just gone three, but it was quite dark already.

The door of Scrooge's counting house was open, that he might keep his eye upon his clerk, who, in a dismal little cell beyond, a sort of tank, was copying letters. Scrooge had a very small fire, but the clerk's fire was so very much smaller that it looked like one coal. But he couldn't replenish it, for Scrooge kept the coal box in his own room. Wherefore the clerk put on his white comforter, and tried to warm himself at the candle; in which effort, not being a man of strong imagination, he failed.

'A Merry Christmas, uncle! God save you!' cried a cheerful voice. It was the voice of Scrooge's nephew.

'Bah!' said Scrooge. 'Humbug!'

'Christmas a humbug, uncle! You don't mean that, I am sure?'

'I do. Out upon merry Christmas! What's Christmas time to you but a time for paying bills without money; a time for finding yourself a year older, and not an hour richer; a time for balancing your books and having every item in 'em through a round dozen of months presented dead against you? If I had my will, every idiot who goes about with "Merry Christmas" on his lips should be boiled with his own pudding, and buried

with a stake of holly through his heart. He should!'

* * *

However, these are Scrooge's views before he is visited by the ghostly form of his old partner, Jacob Marley, who is now suffering for a lifetime's meanness and who warns him to repent, before it is too late. In this second extract, the ghost of Christmas Present shows him what is happening at the house of his own clerk, Bob Cratchit.

* * *

Then up rose Mrs Cratchit, dressed out but poorly in a twice-turned gown, but brave in ribbons, which are cheap and make a goodly show for sixpence; and she laid the cloth, assisted by Belinda Cratchit, second of her daughters, also brave in ribbons; while Master Peter Cratchit plunged a fork into a saucepan of potatoes, and getting the corners of his monstrous shirt collar (Bob's private property, conferred upon his son in honour of the day) into his mouth, rejoiced to find himself so gallantly attired. And now, two smaller Cratchits came tearing in, screaming that outside the bakers they had smelt the goose and known it for their own. . . .

'Whatever has got into your precious father then?' said Mrs Cratchit. 'And your brother, Tiny Tim! And Martha wasn't as late last Christmas day by half an hour!'

'Here's Martha, mother!' cried the two young Cratchits. 'Hurrah! There's such a goose, Martha!'

'Why, bless your heart alive, my dear, how late you are!' said Mrs Cratchit, kissing her daughter a dozen times.

'We'd a deal of work to finish up last night,' replied the girl, 'and had to clear up this morning, mother.'

In came Bob, the father, with at least three feet of comforter, excluding the fringe, hanging down before him; and his threadbare clothes darned up and brushed, to look seasonable; and Tiny Tim upon his shoulder. Alas for Tiny Tim, he bore a little crutch, and had his limbs supported by an iron frame!

'And how did little Tim behave?' asked Mrs Cratchit.

'As good as gold,' said Bob, 'and better. Somehow he gets thoughtful, sitting by himself so much, and he thinks the strangest things. He told me, coming home, that he hoped the people saw him in church, because he was a cripple and they might remember, upon Christmas Day, who made lame beggars walk and blind men see.'

Bob's voice was tremulous when he told them this and trembled more when he said that Tiny Tim should grow strong and hearty . . .

There never was such a goose. Bob said he didn't believe that there ever was such a goose cooked. Its tenderness and flavour, size and cheapness, were the themes of universal admiration. Eked out by mashed potatoes and apple sauce it was a sufficient dinner for the whole family and the youngest Cratchits in particular were steeped in sage and onion to the eyebrows! But now, the plates being changed by Miss Belinda, Mrs Cratchit left the room alone – too nervous to bear witnesses – to take the pudding up, and bring it in.

Suppose it should not be done

enough! Suppose it should break in turning out! All sorts of horrors were supposed.

Hello! A great deal of steam! The pudding was out of the copper. A smell like washing day! That was the cloth. A smell like an eating house and a pastry cook's next door to each other, with a laundress's next door to that! That was the pudding! In half a minute, Mrs Cratchit entered – flushed but smiling proudly – with the pudding, like a speckled cannon ball.

Oh, what a wonderful pudding! Bob Cratchit said that he regarded it as the greatest success achieved by Mrs Cratchit since their marriage. Mrs Cratchit said that now the weight was off her mind, she would confess she had had her doubts about the quantity of flour. Everybody had something to say about it, but nobody said or thought it was at all a small pudding for such a large family. Any Cratchit would have blushed to hint at such a thing.

At last, the dinner was all done, the cloth was cleared and all the Cratchit family drew round the hearth in what Bob Cratchit called a circle, and at Bob Cratchit's elbow stood the family display of glass – two tumblers and a custard cup without a handle. These held the hot punch as well as golden goblets would have done; and Bob served it out with beaming looks, while the chestnuts on the fire spluttered and cracked noisily. Then Bob proposed: 'A Merry Christmas to all of us, my dears. God bless us!'

Which all the family re-echoed. 'God bless us every one!' said Tiny Tim.

* * *

Scrooge has been disturbed by an earlier vision of himself as a boy, when Christmas still held its magic and he is stirred even more at the sight of the Cratchits' contentment with such a small feast. He is particularly upset at the sight of little, crippled Tiny Tim, and the realization that the little boy will die without warmth and proper food.

However, his change of heart is complete when he sees the vision of Christmas Yet to Come. This shows a neglected grave of a man who was hated and despised in his life – and he realizes that the grave is his own! Immediately, Scrooge decides to change his fate. He sets about making the Cratchits' Christmas a really happy one as soon as his clerk arrives back at work. (Bob Cratchit's Christmas holiday only consisted of one day, reluctantly allowed.) You will be pleased to hear that in fact, Tiny Tim does not die.

# WELCOME YULE!

Now, thrice welcome Christmas,
Which brings us good cheer,
Minced pies and plum porridge,
Good ale and strong beer;
With pig, goose, and capon,
The best that can be,
So well doth the weather
And our stomachs agree.

With holly and ivy
So green and so gay,
We deck up our houses
As fresh as the day.
With bays and rosemary,
And laurel complete;
And everyone now
Is a king in conceit.

From the poem by George Wither

# Twelve Days of Christmas

Should auld acquaintance be forgot,
And never brought to mind?
Should auld acquaintance be forgot
For the sake of auld lang syne?

For auld lang syne, my dear,
For auld lang syne,
We'll drink a cup of kindness yet
For auld lang syne.

# THE TWELVE DAYS OF CHRISTMAS

On the first day of Christmas, my true love sent to me
A partridge in a pear-tree.

On the second day of Christmas, my true love sent to me
Two turtle doves and a partridge in a pear tree.

On the third day of Christmas, my true love sent to me
Three French hens,
Two turtle doves, and a partridge in a pear tree.

On the fourth day of Christmas, my true love sent to me
Four colly birds, three French hens,
Two turtle doves, and a partridge in a pear tree.

On the fifth day of Christmas, my true love sent to me
Five gold rings,
Four colly birds, three French hens,
Two turtle doves, and a partridge in a pear tree.

On the sixth day of Christmas, my true love sent to me
Six geese a-laying, five gold rings,
Four colly birds, three French hens,
Two turtle doves, and a partridge in a pear tree.

On the seventh day of Christmas, my true love sent to me
Seven swans a-swimming,
Six geese a-laying, five gold rings,
Four colly birds, three French hens,
Two turtle doves, and a partridge in a pear tree.

On the eighth day of Christmas, my true love sent to me
Eight maids a-milking, seven swans a-swimming,
Six geese a-laying, five gold rings,
Four colly birds, three French hens,
Two turtle doves, and a partridge in a pear tree.

On the ninth day of Christmas, my true love sent to me
Nine drummers drumming,
Eight maids a-milking, seven swans a-swimming,
Six geese a-laying, five gold rings,
Four colly birds, three French hens,
Two turtle doves, and a partridge in a pear tree.

On the tenth day of Christmas, my true love sent to me
Ten pipers piping, nine drummers drumming,
Eight maids a-milking, seven swans a-swimming,
Six geese a-laying, five gold rings,
Four colly birds, three French hens,
Two turtle doves, and a partridge in a pear tree.

On the eleventh day of Christmas, my true love sent to me
Eleven ladies dancing,
Ten pipers piping, nine drummers drumming,
Eight maids a-milking, seven swans a-swimming,
Six geese a-laying, five gold rings,
Four colly birds, three French hens,
Two turtle doves, and a partridge in a pear tree.

On the twelfth day of Christmas, my true love sent to me
Twelve lords a-leaping, eleven ladies dancing,
Ten pipers piping, nine drummers drumming,
Eight maids a-milking, seven swans a-swimming,
Six geese a-laying, five gold rings,
Four colly birds, three French hens,
Two turtle doves, and a partridge in a pear tree.

Traditional

# THE OLD YEAR HAS PASSED

In Scotland, the New Year means a lot of celebrations. Long before Robert Burns wrote 'Auld lang syne', the English have tended to cast a wistful eye at the festivities north of the border.

At midnight on New Year's Eve, the head of the house opened wide the door to let the Old Year out and everyone shouted or crashed pots and trays to make sure that any lurking evil spirits had been chased away. The first person to come in (the 'first foot') would decide the luck of the house for the whole of the next twelve months. A huge responsibility, and one which some people did not leave to chance. They rigged it so that the right sort of first foot arrived – a dark-haired man with perfect sight and eyebrows that had no possibility of meeting in the middle. Women, you may notice, were not lucky!

The first footer should carry a piece of coal, some money (or a piece of bread) and some mistletoe. He should enter in silence, put the coal on the fire, the money on the table and the mistletoe on the mantelpiece. He then wishes everyone 'Happy New Year' and in return gets a glass of whisky and a kiss or as many of each as he can manage.

In some places, they have a huge fire to burn away the Old Year and people eat black bun (a rich fruit cake) and treacle bannocks.

In England, there was always some kind of a play or masque or musical at Christmas and this tradition still lingers in Pantomime. Pantomime itself only belongs to the last century and characters like the Dame come straight out of Victorian music hall, together with all the wonderful slapstick and 'magic'.

Twelfth Night, the last day of the Christmas celebrations, was once one of the most important. (Why twelve days of Christmas? No one knows for sure; but perhaps it was something to do with the Twelve Disciples of Jesus.) It was the feast of the Three Kings and marked the day that Caspar, Melchior and Balthazar brought their gifts of gold, frankincense and myrrh to baby Jesus.

But there are other traditions, even older, such as the Twelfth Night Cake. Hidden in this cake would be a bean and a pea. The man who found the bean became the Twelfth Night 'King' and the woman who found the pea, the 'Queen'. They would take the lead in all the evening's celebrations and of course, it meant that they had twelve months of good luck ahead of them. More recently, we began putting silver sixpences in the Christmas pudding instead!

Twelfth Night is the time when we should take down Christmas decorations to avoid bad luck. It used to be said that however many holly leaves had been left up by the next day, the same number of goblins would be seen by the family in the year to come!

# THE OLD YEAR

The Old Year's gone away
To nothingness and night;
We cannot find him all the day
Nor hear him in the night.
He left no footstep, mark or place
In either shade or sun.
The last year he'd a neighbour's face.
In this he's known by none.

Old papers thrown away,
Old garments cast aside,
The talk of yesterday,
All things identified;
But times once torn away
No voices can recall;
The eve of New Year's Day
Left the Old Year lost to all.

From the poem by John Clare

# A NEW YEAR'S EVE PARTY

ABRIDGED FROM *LITTLE WOMEN*
BY LOUISA M. ALCOTT

JO! Jo! where are you?' cried Meg, at the foot of the attic stairs. Running up, Meg found her sister crying over her favourite book, wrapped up in a sweater on an old three-legged sofa. This was Jo's favourite place.

'Such fun! look! an invitation from Mrs Gardiner for tomorrow night!' cried Meg, waving the precious paper. '"Mrs Gardiner would be happy to see Miss March and Miss Josephine at a little party on New Year's Eve." Marmee is willing we should go; now what shall we wear?'

'What's the use of asking that, when you know we shall wear our poplins because we haven't got anything else?' answered Jo, with her mouth full of apple.

'If I only had a silk!' sighed Meg. 'Mother says I may when I'm eighteen, perhaps; but two years is an everlasting time to wait.'

'I'm sure our pops look like silk, and they are nice enough. Yours is as good as new, but I forgot the burn and the tear in mine. Whatever shall I do? The burn shows badly.'

'You must sit still all you can, and keep your back out of sight; the front is all right. I shall have a ribbon for my hair, and Marmee will lend me her little pearl pin, and my new slippers are lovely, and my gloves will do, though they aren't as nice as I'd like.'

'Mine are spoilt with lemonade, and I can't get any new ones so I shall have to go without,' said Jo, who never bothered much about clothes.

'You must have gloves, or I won't go,' cried Meg. 'They are more important than anything else. I should be so very ashamed if you didn't have them.'

'I can hold them crumpled up in my hand, so no one will know how stained they are; that's all I can do. No, I'll tell you how we can manage – each wear one good one and carry a bad one; don't you see?'

'Your hands are bigger than mine, and you will stretch my glove dreadfully,' began Meg, whose gloves were a tender point with her.

'Then I'll go without. I don't care what people say!' cried Jo.

'You can have it, you can! Only don't stain it, and do behave nicely. Don't push your hands behind you, or stare or talk slang, will you?'

'Don't worry about me; I'll be as prim as I can.'

So Meg went away to 'accept with thanks', look over her dress, and sing happily as she did up her one real lace frill; while Jo finished her story and her four apples.

On New Year's Eve the two younger girls watched while the two older were deep in the all-important business of 'getting ready for the party'. There was a great deal of running up and down, laughing and talking. Meg wanted a few curls about her face, and Jo pinched the papered locks with a pair of hot tongs.

'Ought they to smoke like that?' asked Beth, from her perch on the bed.

'It's the dampness drying,' replied Jo.

'What an odd smell! It's like burnt feathers,' said Amy, smoothing her own pretty curls.

'There, now I'll take off the papers and you'll see a cloud of little ringlets,' said Jo, putting down the tongs.

She did take off the papers, but no cloud of ringlets appeared, for the hair came off with the papers, and the horrified hair-dresser laid a row of little scorched bundles on the table before her victim. 'Oh, oh, oh! what have you done? It's ruined! I can't go! My hair, oh my hair!' wailed Meg, looking with despair at the uneven frizzle on her forehead.

'Just my luck; you shouldn't have asked me to do it; I always spoil everything. I'm so sorry, but the tongs were too hot, and so I've made a mess,' groaned poor Jo, looking at the black pancakes almost in tears.

'It isn't spoilt: just frizzle it, and tie your ribbon so the ends come on your forehead a bit, and it will look like the last fashion. I've seen many girls do it,' said Amy, consolingly.

'Serves me right for trying to be fine. I wish I'd let my hair alone,' cried Meg.

'So do I, it was so smooth and pretty. But it will soon grow out again,' said Beth, coming to kiss and comfort the shorn sheep.

Meg was finished at last, and even Jo's hair was got up and her dress on. They looked very well in their simple suits. Meg in silvery grey, with a blue velvet edging, lace frills, and the pearl pin; Jo in maroon, with a stiff, gentlemanly linen collar and a white chrysanthemum. Each put on one nice light glove, and carried one dirty one. Meg's high-heeled slippers were very tight, and hurt her, though she would not own it, and Jo's nineteen hair-pins all seemed stuck straight into her head, which was not exactly comfortable; but, dear me let us be elegant or die!

'Have a good time, dears!' said Mrs March. 'And come away at eleven.' As the gate clashed behind them, a voice cried from a window –

'Girls, girls! have you both got nice pocket-handkerchiefs?'

'Yes, yes, and Meg has scent on hers,' cried Jo, adding with a laugh, as they went on. 'I do believe Marmee would ask that if we were all running away from an earthquake.'

'Now don't forget to keep the burn out of sight, Jo. Is my sash right? and does my hair look very bad?' said Meg, as she turned from the glass in Mrs Gardiner's dressing-room after a prolonged prink.

'I know I shall forget. If you see me doing anything wrong just remind me by a wink, will you?' returned Jo, giving her collar a twitch and her hair a hasty brush.

'No, winking isn't lady-like; I'll lift my eyebrows if anything is wrong, and nod if you are all right. Now hold your shoulders straight, and take short steps, and don't shake hands if you are introduced to any one: it isn't the thing.'

'How do you learn all the proper ways? I never can.'

Down they went, feeling a little shy, for they seldom went to parties. Mrs Gardiner, a stately old lady, greeted them kindly, and handed them over to the eldest of her six daughters. Meg knew Sallie, and was at her ease very soon; but Jo, who didn't care much for girls or girlish gossip, stood about, with her back carefully against the wall, and felt as much out of place as a colt in a flower-garden.

No one came to talk to her and she could not roam about and amuse herself, for the burnt dress would show; so she stared at the people rather forlornly till the dancing began. Meg was asked at once, and the tight slippers tripped about so briskly that none would have guessed the pain their wearer suffered smilingly. Jo saw a big red-headed youth approaching her corner, and afraid he wanted to dance, she slipped into a curtained recess. Unfortunately, another shy person had chosen the same hiding place; and she found herself face to face with the 'Laurence boy'.

'Oh dear, I didn't know any one was here!' stammered Jo.

But the boy laughed, and said pleasantly – 'Don't mind me; stay if you like, Miss March.'

'Sha'n't I disturb you?'

'Not a bit; I only came here because I don't know many people, and I felt rather strange at first, you know.'

'So did I. Don't go away, please, unless you'd rather.'

The boy sat down again and looked at his shoes till Jo said, trying to be polite, 'I think I've had the pleasure of seeing you before; you live near us don't you?'

'Next door'; and he looked up and laughed outright, for Jo's prim manner was rather funny.

That put Jo at her ease; she said, in her most cheerful way, 'I'm not Miss March, I'm only Jo.'

'I'm not Mr Laurence, I'm only Laurie.'

Then they both peeped and criticized and chatted, till they felt like old friends. Laurie's shyness soon wore off; for Jo's boyish manner set him at his ease, and Jo was her merry self again, because her dress was forgotten, and nobody lifted their eyebrows at her.

She liked the 'Laurence boy' better than ever, and took several good looks at him, so that she might describe him to the girls; for they had no brothers and boys were almost unknown creatures to them. 'Curly black hair; brown skin; big, black eyes; handsome nose; taller than I am; and altogether nice. Wonder how old he is?'

It was on the tip of Jo's tongue to ask; but she checked herself in time, and with unusual tact, tried to find out in a roundabout way.

'I suppose you are going to college soon?'

'Not for a year or two; I won't go before seventeen, anyway.'

'Are you only fifteen?' asked Jo, looking at the tall lad, whom she had imagined seventeen already.

'Sixteen, next month.'

'How I wish I was going to college! You don't look as if you like it!'

'I hate it!'

Jo wanted very much to ask what he would like: but his black brows looked rather threatening; so she changed the subject and said, 'That's a splendid piano in the next room. Why don't you go and try it?'

'If you will come too,' he answered, with a gallant little bow.

'I can't; for I told Meg I wouldn't, because. . . .' There Jo stopped, and looked undecided whether to tell or to laugh.

'Because what?' asked Laurie, curiously.

'You won't tell?'

'Never!'

'Well, I have a bad trick of standing before the fire, and so I burn my frocks, and I scorched this one; and though it's nicely mended, it shows, and Meg told me to keep still, so no one would see it. You may laugh, if you want to; it is funny, I know.'

But Laurie didn't laugh; he only looked down a minute, and the expression of his face puzzled Jo, when he said very gently, 'Never mind that. Please come?'

Jo thanked him, and gladly went, wishing she had two neat gloves, when she saw the nice, pearl-coloured ones her partner wore.

Then Meg appeared in search of her sister. She beckoned, and Jo reluctantly followed her into a side room, where she found her on a sofa, holding her foot, and looking pale.

'I've sprained my ankle. That stupid high heel turned. I don't know how I'm ever going to get home,' she said, rocking to and fro in pain.

'I knew you'd hurt your feet with those silly shoes. I'm sorry. But I don't see what you can do, except get a carriage, or stay here all night,' answered Jo, softly rubbing the poor ankle as she spoke.

'I can't have a carriage, without its costing ever so much. I dare say I can't get one at all; for most people come in their own and it's a long way to the stable, and no one to send.'

'I'll go.'

'No, indeed! It's past nine, and pitch dark. I can't stay here, for the house is full. Sallie has some girls staying with her. I'll rest till after supper and then do the best I can.'

'I'll ask Laurie; he will go,' said Jo.

'Mercy, no! Don't ask or tell any one.'

'They are going out to supper now. I'll stay with you; I'd rather.'

'No, run and bring me some coffee. I'm so tired, I can't move!'

So Jo went blundering away to the dining-room. Making a dart at the table she grabbed the coffee, which she immediately spilt, making the front of her dress as bad as the back.

'Oh, dear, what an idiot I am!' cried Jo, finishing off Meg's glove by scrubbing her gown with it.

'Can I help you?' said a friendly voice; and there was Laurie again, with a full cup in one hand, and a plate of ice cream in the other.

'I was trying to get something for Meg, who is very tired, and some one shook me; and here I am, in a mess,' answered Jo, looking from the stained skirt to the coffee-coloured glove.

'Too bad! I was looking for someone to give this to. Can I take it to your sister?'

'Oh, thank you! I'll show you where she is. I'd take it myself but I'd only drop it.'

Jo led the way; and, as if used to waiting on ladies, Laurie drew up a little table, brought a second cup of coffee

and ice for Jo, and was so friendly even Meg pronounced him a 'nice boy'.

They were all talking and laughing and Meg forgot her foot. At ten o'clock she rose so quickly that she was forced to catch hold of Jo, with a cry of pain.

'Hush! Don't say anything,' she whispered, adding aloud, 'It's nothing. I turned my foot a little, that's all'; and limped upstairs to put her things on.

Meg cried, and Jo was at her wits' end, till she decided to take things into her own hands. Slipping out, she ran down and asked where she could find a carriage. Laurie, who had heard what she said, came up, and offered his grandfather's carriage, which had just come for him.

'It's so early! You can't mean to go yet?' began Jo, looking relieved, but hesitating to accept the offer.

'I always go early – I do, really! Please let me take you home. It's all on my way, you know, and anyway it's raining.'

That settled it; and, telling him of Meg's ankle, Jo gratefully accepted, and rushed up to bring down her sister and they rolled away in the luxurious carriage, feeling very festive and grand. Laurie went on the box; so Meg could keep her foot up, and the girls talked over their party in freedom.

'I had a great time. Did you?' asked Jo, rumpling up her hair, and making herself comfortable.

'Yes, till I hurt myself. Sallie's friend, Annie Moffat, asked me to spend a week with her when Sallie does. It will be perfectly splendid, if mother only lets me go,' answered Meg, cheering up at the thought.

'I saw you with the red-headed man I ran away from. Was he nice?'

'Oh, very! His hair is auburn, not red; and he is very polite.'

'He looked like a grasshopper in a fit. Laurie and I couldn't help laughing. Did you hear us?'

'No; but it was very rude. What were you about all that time, hidden away there?'

By the time Jo had finished telling her adventures they were at home. With many thanks, they said 'Good night', and crept in, hoping to disturb no one; but the instant their door creaked, two sleepy but eager voices cried out – 'Tell about the party! Tell about the party!'

Meg was horrified but Jo had saved some sweets for the little girls; and they soon subsided, after hearing the most thrilling events of the evening.

'I declare, I really feel like a fine young lady coming home from the party in a carriage with someone to look after me,' said Meg, as Jo bandaged up her foot and brushed her hair.

'I don't believe fine ladies enjoy themselves a bit more than we do, in spite of our burnt hair, old dresses, one glove each and tight slippers that sprain our ankles when we are silly enough to wear them,' said Jo.

# KINGS OF ORIENT

We three Kings of Orient are;
Bearing gifts we traverse afar
Field and fountain, moor and mountain
Following yonder star.

O star of wonder, star of night,
Star with royal beauty bright,
Westward leading, still proceeding,
Guide us to thy perfect light.

From the traditional carol

# TWELFTH NIGHT TILL CANDLEMAS

ABRIDGED FROM *TWELFTH NIGHT TILL CANDLEMAS*
BY RUTH PAINE

Once, in Queen Victoria's reign there lived a village schoolmaster, his wife and their children, Robert, Jane, Hugh and little Lucy.

Theirs was a happy home, for Father was kind and patient, and Mother was gentle, cheerful and hard-working.

Across the green, in a little cottage next to the church, lived their Great-Granny Hawkins.

Granny Hawkins always spent Christmas with the family in the schoolhouse. Before she hobbled home on Twelfth Night, she would say:

'Now mind you take down all the holly and the ivy, and the silver bells and paper chains.'

'But they look so pretty,' said Jane, 'we could leave them up for a bit longer, surely!'

'Take them down today!' insisted Granny Hawkins, shaking her stick at Jane.

'Why?' asked Hugh.

'Because if you don't, a demon might come and live in this house, and then there would be trouble!' Granny said.

'Pooh! We don't believe in such things!' scoffed Robert.

Nevertheless, as soon as they had waved Granny Hawkins goodbye, they took down all the greenery, making a bonfire of it in the garden, and put the glittery decorations away in the attic.

But one year they did not notice that a little sprig of holly had fallen on to the dusty top of the old grandfather clock.

That night, all the Twelfth Night witches and goblins and demons began rushing about trying to find a hiding place. Outside, the air was cold and pure from snow and frost and the wicked ones longed for a dark, snug corner indoors. So they peered through windows, and peeped through cracks, spying this way and that with their sharp little eyes.

One evil little demon spotted the holly sprig and straightaway, he slipped in and settled himself under it, making himself small as a holly berry. He chuckled with malice.

Next day, he began making his evil magic. That morning, Father stubbed his toe getting up in the dark and swore loudly. Such a thing had never been known before! Mother woke with a headache. Robert could not find his satchel and accused Hugh of taking it. Hugh tripped on the stairs and sprained

C.T. Garland

his ankle.

Jane, always so careful, broke a plate as she helped wash up and merry, good little Lucy sulked and would not drink her milk. And that was only the beginning!

In the following days, Mother's headaches got worse. Robert, who hoped to win a scholarship to the big town school that summer, could not concentrate on his homework. His sums would not work out, he made spelling mistakes, and got his history dates muddled. Father was angry and shouted at him.

Jane broke a dish every time she washed up, and she pricked her finger when she sewed her sampler and got spots of blood on it. Her neat stitches became great crooked ones that Mother made her unpick, until tear stains mixed with blood spots on the once-beautiful embroidery.

As for Lucy, she threw her porridge on the floor, sucked lumps of coal, and howled to be picked up and cuddled.

'I can't think what has taken her!' said Mother. When the children told all this to Granny Hawkins, she said, 'You have a demon in the house. Are you sure you took down all the Christmas decorations?'

'Of course we did!' the children cried. Father snapped, 'Nonsense! Granny Hawkins is a superstitious old woman.'

Mother said, 'Well, we've never been like this before! Oh, dear! My head aches so!'

The horrid little demon under the holly sprig on top of the clock jeered at them.

Things got even worse. Lucy stopped howling and getting into mischief and became silent, pale and thin. She seemed to fade away. At first the doctor said, 'It's this terrible month of January! She'll pick up when spring comes.' But after a while he shook his head gloomily, puzzled and hopeless.

Robert, Jane and Hugh went across the green to visit their Great-Granny.

'It's a demon, all right!' she said. 'I know the signs. But soon it will be February the second. Do you know what day that is?'

The children looked at her blankly.

'No, you wouldn't!' she muttered. It was terrible how ignorant children were nowadays about important things!

'It's Candlemas,' she explained. 'If you don't get him out then, you're saddled with him for the rest of the year.'

'What's Candlemas?' asked Hugh.

Granny Hawkins said, 'Long ago people went to church with lighted candles for the priest to bless. There's nothing like a Candlemas candle for driving out the wicked ones! Let's go and see the Vicar. Perhaps he will let us keep Candlemas properly this year.'

But the Vicar shook his head. 'No, no, my dear Mrs Hawkins. My churchwardens would say it is gross superstition.'

Granny Hawkins and the children went sadly away. But as they reached the gate, the Vicar came running after them.

'I've just remembered,' he puffed. 'This year, Candlemas falls on a Sunday. Now, if you children come to the evening service, I shall give a blessing, as usual. If you have candles with you – hidden away, not lighted, of course – well, I suppose you may think I have blessed your candles!'

And that is exactly what they did. After the service, they lit the candles and placed them around the house. And immediately, the little demon dashed out through the keyhole as fast as he could go.

Next day was spring-like, with snowdrops bright in the garden. Mother's headache had vanished, and Father was his usual kindly self. Robert's brain had cleared, and when Father said, 'We must work hard together to get you that scholarship, for I know you can do it,' he was sure he could.

Jane broke no more dishes and the sampler was finished and hung on the wall. Hugh was just as good at sport as ever and Lucy was soon as merry and well as before.

Father said, 'The doctor was right! We all feel better now spring is here.' But Granny Hawkins and the children knew it was the Candlemas candles.

Mother said the sunshine showed up the dust and she must begin spring cleaning. When she cleaned the top of the grandfather clock, she found a dusty sprig of holly, which she quickly threw on the fire. But not before Jane had seen it.

'So that was it,' Jane thought.

'Of course,' said Granny Hawkins, when Jane told her about it.

mained silent. 'Aren't I going to do anything?' But of course it had joined in. It had done all it had to do.

And the man told them about Humpty-Dumpty. The children clapped their hands and cried, 'Tell us another! Tell us another!'

They wanted *Puss in Boots*. The fir-tree stood quite still and thoughtful. The birds out in the forest had never told him anything like that. 'Humpty-Dumpty fell down the stairs and for all that won the princess. Yes, yes, that's how the world goes!' thought the fir-tree, who believed it was all true because it was such a nice man who had told the story. 'Yes, who knows? Perhaps I shall fall down the stairs, too, and win a princess!' And it looked forward to being dressed up again the next day with candles and toys and gold and fruit.

'I shan't tremble tomorrow,' it thought. 'I'll enjoy myself properly in all my glory. Tomorrow I shall hear the story of Humpty-Dumpty again, and perhaps the one about Puss in Boots as well.' And the tree stood there quiet and thoughtful the whole night through.

Sadly, this was the little fir-tree's moment of glory and the next morning, it was put into the attic with only the mice for company. Finally, it was taken out into the yard to be burned. But the story is not quite as sad as it seems:

The tree looked at the flowers, beautiful and fresh in the garden – it looked at itself, and wished it had stayed in its dark corner in the attic. It thought of its own fresh youth in the forest, of the merry Christmas Eve and of the little mice who had listened with such delight to the story of Humpty Dumpty.

'Gone! Gone!' said the poor little tree. 'If only I'd been happy when I could! Gone! Gone!'

And the man servant came and chopped the tree into small pieces until a whole pile lay there. It blazed beautifully under the big copper; and it sighed so deeply, each sigh like a pistol shot, that the children who were playing ran in and, sitting in front of the fire, looked into it and cried 'Pop! Pop!' But with each crack – really a deep sigh – the tree thought upon a summer's day in the forest or a winter's night when the stars were shining. It thought of Christmas Eve and Humpty Dumpty, the only fairy tale it had ever heard and knew how to tell – and then the tree was burned up.

The boys played in the yard, and the smallest of them wore upon his chest the gold star which the little tree had worn on its happiest evening. It was gone now, the tree was gone too, and its story was over – as stories are, sooner or later.

# WHEN ICICLES HANG BY THE WALL

When icicles hang by the wall,
And Dick the shepherd blows his nail,
And Tom bears logs into the hall,
And milk comes frozen home in pail,
When blood is nipp'd and ways be foul;
Then nightly sings the staring owl,
To-whit!
To-who! – a merry note,
While greasy Joan doth keel the pot.

When all aloud the wind doth blow,
And coughing drowns the parson's saw,
And birds sit brooding in the snow,
And Marian's nose looks red and raw,
When roasted crabs hiss in the bowl;
Then nightly sings the staring owl,
To-whit!
To-who! a merry note,
While greasy Joan doth keel the pot.

William Shakespeare

# INDEX

## Stories



## Poems



## Carols



## Fact and Fiction

# ACKNOWLEDGEMENTS

The editor and publishers would like to thank the following for permission to use copyright material in this collection. Every effort has been made to contact copyright holders but this has not always been possible. We would be grateful to hear from anyone who can enable us to correct any omission in this list.

Julie Banyard for the illustration to 'The Father Christmas on the Cake', from *A Moment in Rhyme*, first published by Century Hutchinson Ltd.

J. M. Dent & Sons Ltd for 'When All the World is Full of Snow' by N. M. Bodecker from *Hurry, Hurry Mary Dear*.

Dorothy Edwards' family for 'My Naughty Little Sister at Christmas', from *The Naughtiest Story Ever* by Dorothy Edwards © Dorothy Edwards, first published by Methuen & Co Ltd.

Faber & Faber Ltd for 'Christmas is Coming', from *A Country Child* by Alison Uttley.

Floris Books for 'Ollie in Winter', from *Ollie's Ski Trip* by Elsa Beskow; A & C Black for the English translation of the text.

David Higham Associates Ltd for 'Christmas among the Savages', from *Christmas with the Savages* by Mary Clive and 'For Them' by Eleanor Farjeon from *Silver Sand and Snow*.

John Murray Publishers Ltd for 'Christmas' by John Betjeman from *Collected Poems*.

Oxford University Press for 'The Stones', reprinted from *French Legends, Tales and Fairy Stories*, retold by Barbara Leonie Picard (1955) and 'The Little Fir Tree' © L W Kingsland 1985, reprinted from *Hans Andersen's Fairy Tales*, translated by L W Kingsland 1985.

Alison Sage for all original material in this collection.

Illustrations on front cover and pages 41, 110 and 117 by courtesy of the Board of Trustees of the Victoria and Albert Museum.

Colin West for 'The Father Christmas on the Cake', from *A Moment in Rhyme*, first published by Century Hutchinson Ltd.